The Tomb
of the Emperor

Penn Mullin

High Noon Books
Novato, California

Cover Design and Interior Illustrations: Nancy Peach

International Standard Book Number: 1-57128-060-X

10 09 08 07 06 05 04 03
9   8   7   6   5

Contents

Corina and Zack are young co-workers at the Park Museum. They are assistants to the museum's director, Claire Long, who sends them to the "four corners of the world" on exciting explorations.

CHAPTER 1

A New Discovery!

"Corina, they are opening a new burial pit in China! I just saw the news on the net," Zack said. "Wouldn't it be great if we could go over and see it? My college friend Wu Hong works for the museum right there in Xian (Shawn). I'll e-mail him and see if he needs any extra help!"

"I would *love* to go over there!" Corina looked over Zack's shoulder at the computer screen that showed a picture of a huge pit. "I wonder what they will find in this one. It's so amazing what the emperors of China did 2000 years ago – making whole *life-size* armies out of clay and burying them in these huge pits. Soldiers in rows, battle ready."

"The emperors wanted these armies to protect them in the afterlife when they died," Zack said. "But at least these soldiers were made of clay! Some emperors buried their armies *alive*!"

"Hurry and e-mail your friend!" Corina said. "If he says O.K., then all we have to do is get Claire to let us go!"

"It's amazing what the emperors of China did 2000 years ago – making whole life-size armies out of clay and burying them in these huge pits. Soldiers in rows, battle ready."

3

CHAPTER 2

Welcome to China!

"I'm ready to get off this airplane!" Zack said as he stretched. "I was ready two hours ago when we changed planes in Beijing (Bay-SHING). China is a *long* way from America!"

"Claire hates long plane trips. No wonder she decided not to come. But I think she was tempted. With your friend Wu opening a new pit here," said Corina.

Zack laughed. "I'm thinking about the last thing Claire said before we left. 'Just try to have a *normal* trip for a change. No mysteries, cave-ins, robbers! Go see the burial pits. Try to arrange to borrow some clay soldiers for a show at our museum! That's all!'"

"That's all!" Corina chuckled. "Maybe Claire is *afraid* to come with us. So many weird things seem to happen."

The plane's loud speaker suddenly came on with a message in Chinese and then in English: "We will be landing in Xian in ten minutes. Please fasten your seatbelts."

"Almost there!" Corina put away her laptop computer and looked out the window. "It is so flat down there. Field after field of crops. With a big hill now and then."

Zack looked down over her shoulder. "Those 'hills' are the emperors' tombs. I've seen pictures of them. The pits of buried clay soldiers are all around them. Look! There's one. It has a big tent over it."

The plane soon touched down lightly on the runway at Xian and taxied to a stop.

"I'm glad Wu will meet us," Zack said. "It's been a long time since I've seen him!"

"Uh-oh, Zack," Corina laughed. "Don't forget your laptop!" She shook her pretty black hair and started down the aisle.

A sea of faces waited at the gate. Suddenly a tall handsome young man came towards them with a welcoming smile.

"Zack! How good to see you!" Wu shook Zack's hand happily. "I am so glad you are here. And this pretty lady is Corina?" Wu bowed before her.

"So pleased to meet you, Wu," Corina smiled. "I've heard a lot about you."

"I hope none of the *bad* stories," Wu laughed. "We were wild in college. But now we're serious museum workers, right, Zack?"

"Sounds like you *do* have a serious job here – in charge of the burial pits!" Zack said.

"It is exciting – we are finding new things all the time," Wu said. "I am so glad you can be here to see the new pit opened!"

They walked out to Wu's car, loaded up,

and started off into the heavy traffic.

"I can't believe all the people here – all the bicycles and cars!" said Corina.

Wu laughed. "Remember – 1 in 5 human beings in the world is Chinese! My country has over a billion people now!"

"All on this road!" Zack laughed.

"We are very near one of the burial pits. I will take you there on the way to your hotel," Wu said. He turned off the busy road. "These pits were found in 1990 when the airport road was being built. The road goes right by the tomb of the emperor Jing Di (Die), who lived about 2100 years ago. The workers thought the soil looked strange and called us in. We found beautiful 2-foot-high pottery soldiers standing guard in long pits. The emperor's army for his afterlife. Look! There is Jing Di's tomb." He pointed to a large green mound in the distance across the fields. "The smaller mound over there belongs to his empress."

"Are these tombs open?" Zack asked.

"No," Wu answered. "They will remain untouched. And this is as it should be. The secrets of the emperor will stay secret."

CHAPTER 3

An Army of Clay

"Look at this!" gasped Corina. She stood beside a long shallow pit that held row after row of brown clay soldiers – each 2 feet high.

"These are the ones we have worked on," Wu explained. "Carefully cutting away the dirt from around their beautiful faces."

Corina and Zack followed Wu down into the pit that was covered by a low roof. Guards waved to Wu. They were there to keep the public away from the clay soldiers.

Wu, Corina, and Zack knelt down beside one of the small doll-like soldiers standing in the pit. "Isn't he beautiful?" Wu said. "See how each man's face is different from the next? This one looks worried. This one happy. No two faces are alike. Jing Di had them carved to look like his real soldiers."

"I bet those soldiers were happy about that," Zack said. "Then they knew they themselves would not be buried in the pit!"

"Maybe Claire will let us come work with you awhile, Wu," Corina laughed. "Your daily work sounds a lot more exciting than ours!"

"It sounds like it, but there are also many, many hours of hard, detailed work," Wu said.

"Scraping all day with a tiny knife or brush just to uncover one little face." Wu smiled. "But when you are done and see what you have found, it is – yes, very exciting!"

"What happened to the arms of the soldiers?" Zack asked Wu.

"They were made of wood, which rotted away over the 2000 years. Just like their silk clothes did," Wu said. "The soldiers' main bodies were made of clay. Damp clay was pressed into wooden molds that were soldier shaped. Then the molds were baked in a wood-fired kiln, or oven, 300 at a time, for 4 days," Wu explained. "Next the statues went to workshops to be painted. Arms were put on and

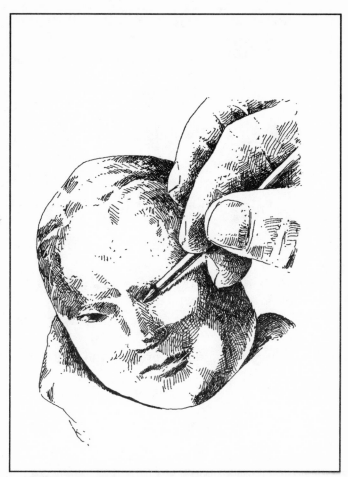

"There are many, many hours of hard, detailed work. Scraping all day with a tiny knife or brush just to uncover one little face."

13

the soldiers were dressed in silk. Then they were given their iron swords, ready to defend their emperor."

"Was Jing Di a good emperor?" Zack asked.

"The main thing he did for China was to place all power in the central government," said Wu. "He ruled in the years 157-141 B.C., during the Han Dynasty. This was a special time when poetry was greatly prized, and paper was invented. The famous Silk Road for trade was set up and started right here."

"That went all the way to India and Rome, didn't it?" said Corina.

"Yes, they sent silk, tea, iron, and steel to

trade for spices, trees, grains. Many new religions like Buddhism entered China through the Silk Road, too," Wu told them. "It was indeed a golden age then. But the golden age had its dark side, too."

"What do you mean?" Zack asked.

"Well, the human cost to keep that rich life going was very great. We found a graveyard over by Jing Di's tomb," Wu said. "In it were the skeletons of about 10,000 men who died building his tomb. Many of them had chains attached to their necks and legs. Some of them had been chopped in half! That was just the way things were then. The dark side of the golden Han Dynasty."

CHAPTER 4

A Secret

"Ah. I'm stuffed!" Zack said as he leaned back from the table. "I have never had fried duck before. That was wonderful. And those pork buns! I just couldn't stop!"

"'The bottomless pit' we call him at the museum," Corina laughed.

"I'm glad you like this restaurant. I come here often when I am in Xian," Wu said. "But I have been so busy I don't have time to eat out much now. Lots of security problems at the new pit."

"Do you need more guards?" Zack asked.

"No, not yet. But I will need them soon. You cannot keep a new pit a secret. You saw it on the Internet. But there is something about this new pit that we want to keep quiet," Wu whispered. "The old histories tell of a special 'emperor's life guard' dressed in jewels and gold. We have never been able to find these soldiers. But I think we are close. And the secret has leaked out. As they always do. And now the wrong people know. It makes me worried. I don't want anyone to get hurt."

"Is there some way we can help with all this?" Zack asked his friend.

"You can be extra pairs of eyes for me at

the pit," Wu said. "Watch to see if there are strange people hanging around."

"You should get back to the museum!" Corina told Wu. "I am worried about what might be going on."

"You're right. I need to get back. But I will take you to your hotel first," Wu said.

"Sounds great!" Zack yawned. "And dinner has finished me off!"

"Xian is such a beautiful city," Corina said. "Thanks for driving us around, Wu. I loved the old pagodas (pa-GO-das), the temples, the wall around the city. I can see why the emperors all chose to live here."

"The old name for this city was Changan

(shang-gone), meaning 'everlasting peace,'" Wu said. "Home of the emperors for 1100 years. Once a center of importance in China."

Wu brought them to a small hotel set in the middle of a forest of pines. The sound of tinkling wind chimes carried on the breeze.

"I'll pick you up early tomorrow morning and take you out to the pit," Wu told Corina and Zack as he helped them check in.

"Good thing we are not going to the pit right now, Zack," Corina laughed. "You're so sleepy I'm afraid you'd fall in!"

CHAPTER 5

The Empire of Qin (Kin)

"Was there any trouble last night at the new pit?" Corina asked Wu the next morning. They were on their way to Wu's museum in his car.

"All quiet. No problems. But today we will know what is in the pit. And then we may have trouble," Wu said worriedly. "If these soldiers are wearing jewels and gold. Look, there's the museum ahead!"

They looked out towards huge curved roofs covering long low buildings in a field.

"The pits are under those roofs, to protect the clay soldiers," Wu told them. "A little different kind of museum."

"This is great, Wu! What a place to work!" Corina said.

"The new pit is far over to the right. With the tent over it," Wu said. "And there's emperor Qin's (Kin's) tomb." He pointed to a large earth mound in the distance.

"How were the clay soldiers discovered?" Zack asked Wu.

"By accident, as always. Some farmers were digging a well here in this peaceful field," said Wu. "And suddenly they came to a clay soldier about 15 feet down!"

"Think of suddenly seeing a life-size head pop out of the ground!" Corina said.

"Well, that soldier was the first of thousands that have been dug up here since 1974," Wu said. He drove into a parking lot near one of the covered pits.

They walked around the long lines of tourists and into the huge outer room. Then they saw it. An army of life-size clay soldiers and horses in long battle lines.

Zack whistled. "This is amazing!"

"They have been standing guard for 2200 years," Wu said. "See how they all face towards Qin's tomb, ready to meet an attack?"

"And they're all in armor, helmets!" said

Corina. "Can we go down closer to them, Wu?"

They followed Wu down into the pit.

"Look how tall they are!" Corina said. "And each face is different. Look, this guy has a great mustache! And I love this beard!"

"We've had to prop up a lot of these soldiers and put them back together. The wooden roofs caved in on this underground battlefield long ago," Wu said.

"These horses are beautiful!" Zack reached out to touch the smooth clay face of the animal. "So lifelike!"

"Their wooden chariots have rotted away. And they once wore leather and brass harnesses, too," said Wu. "Qin wanted the best! He ordered the building of his tomb when he was only 13, in 246 B.C." Wu looked towards the mound in the distance. "700,000 men worked on that underground palace for 36 years! Like Jing Di's tomb, it is still unopened."

"Qin is the emperor who built the Great Wall, isn't he?" asked Zack.

"Yes. You *must* go see it. Not far north of here. Qin built it to protect his empire. It is 1,500 miles long! They call it 'the longest cemetery in the world.' Thousands of people died building it," Wu said. "Their bones were crushed and buried inside it."

"Didn't Qin build it wide enough for 6 horses to run in a row on top?" Zack asked.

"That's right," chuckled Wu. "Qin's lucky number was 6. He was a greatly feared man, but he did change China forever in some good ways. He brought all China together, gave it one central written language. He built great roads and waterways. But he wanted control of everything. He burned books he did not like and buried great writers and thinkers alive!"

"It makes me shiver!" Corina said.

"Qin went sort of crazy later on," Wu said. "He had 270 palaces built for himself around Changan. He was so worried about people trying to kill him that he changed palaces every night! Only two people knew where he slept. If you told where he was, you died!"

CHAPTER 6

Danger in the Pit!

"They've been digging for three hours now," Zack said. "Any minute I bet they'll come to a soldier down there."

He and Corina stood under the small tent above Wu's new pit, watching the workers. Wu was down in the pit, too, directing the digging. There was a feeling of excitement in the air here. What would they find?

"Everybody looks as if they belong to the museum," Corina said. "No strange guys hanging around. Maybe Wu is worrying too much about the pit's being robbed."

"I think he knows more than he's telling us," Zack said. "There are probably some big-time crooks who have their eye on this dig."

Suddenly they saw the workers stop digging. Everybody's eyes were on Wu. He was kneeling in the dirt and looking closely at something. Then he let out a soft whoop of joy and shook his fist!

"He's found something!" Zack said.

He and Corina climbed down into the pit and joined the crowd around Wu. All the workers were talking excitedly in Chinese. Finally Corina and Zack were beside Wu. And there sticking up out of the dirt was the top of a clay head! And the head wore a helmet that was covered with jewels!

"We got lucky!" Wu smiled happily. "Let's keep digging," he told his men. "Look, Corina and Zack, the jewels under this dirt!"

"Amazing! Wu, you've made history!" Zack said. "Can we help you with the digging?"

"No, thanks," Wu answered. "Just be my lookouts until the guards get here. This treasure pit won't stay a secret long."

Just then they all three looked up above the pit. And they saw two men who had not been there a few minutes before. Two men who stared down at them and then disappeared.

There sticking up out of the dirt was the top of a clay head! And the head wore a helmet that was covered with jewels!

CHAPTER 7

Night Watch

Darkness was falling and the men were still digging in the pit under the tent. Corina and Zack watched as Wu and his workers slowly scraped the dirt away from the bodies of two clay soldiers. But these soldiers were dressed in armor painted with pure gold. They wore rings and arm bands made of jewels.

Corina and Zack stood watch for Wu above the pit. Why hadn't the guards come that Wu had called? Soon it would be completely dark.

"Those two strange men give me the creeps," Corina told Zack. "I really hope those guards get here soon."

"Me, too. Those looked like pretty tough guys all right," said Zack. "I wonder who they went to tell and when they will be back!"

Suddenly they heard Wu call out to his workers in the near darkness. Then all the diggers began climbing out of the pit and waving goodnight to Wu.

"What a day!" Wu said as he joined Corina and Zack. "I'm so glad you were here!"

"I'm so proud of you!" Corina told Wu. "I wish we could e-mail Claire and tell her about this. But there's a danger other people might get the message, too."

"Right," Wu said. "Well, thanks for keeping watch. You must be tired – and hungry! My museum friend Wang has gone to bring us some food. Until the guards come we don't dare leave. Those two guys we saw earlier mean trouble," Wu said. "I'll go check about the guards." He walked over to his car phone.

The full moon was slowly rising. The burial tomb of Emperor Qin was a dark shadow in the distant fields. Corina and Zack looked down at the two clay soldiers standing straight and tall at the bottom of the pit.

"They look almost real in the moonlight, don't they?" Zack asked.

"Yes, almost *too* real. I expect them to start walking. Or turn their heads!"

Wu came back from his car. "Bad news. The guards won't get here till morning. There's some trouble in the city and they called in the museum guards to help. So I called the police. They'll send out some men later tonight. But until they get here, we're *it*!"

"Well, we can handle it!" Zack said.

"This is a fine way to treat you two — making you eat dinner in a field and stand watch all night!" Wu told his friends.

Suddenly Corina shivered. Did she hear Wu right? Stand watch *all night*?

"We'll be ready for anything that comes,"

Zack told Wu. "I'm not worried."

What? thought Corina. Three of us way out here guarding a fortune in gold and jewels, without any weapons. And you're not worried?

Suddenly they saw headlights coming towards them in the field. "It's Wang with our dinner. I'll get him to stay here with us," Wu said. They started towards the car.

Wang set out a big feast on a blanket. "Wow! This looks fantastic!" Zack said. "A moonlight picnic! And I've already spotted the fried duck. Wang, thank you!"

Corina began to relax a little and enjoy the meal. Maybe they were all just too jumpy, more worried than they needed to be.

"I think two of us should stand watch while you two sleep," Wu was saying. "Until the police come. Zack, want to take the first watch with me? Corina, you can stretch out in my car if you want. Wang can rest in his car."

"Fine with me," Zack said. "Corina, think you can sleep in the car?"

"*Anywhere* tonight," she said sleepily.

Zack and Wu sat down beside the pit in the moonlight. Corina and Wang each settled into the cars to sleep.

Then Zack was gently shaking Corina, "What?" she mumbled. It couldn't be time to get up. She'd just gone to sleep. He walked her over to where Wang stood by the pit. She and

Wang decided to walk around it to keep themselves awake. The wind had come up now and began to tear at the tent over the pit. Corina stopped at the far end of the pit and stared at the two clay soldiers standing in the moonlight below. Their first night uncovered in nearly 2000 years, she thought to herself. I wonder what they're thinking. Oh, I'm just being a little crazy here. But they look so *alive*. I swear that one just moved. Corina stared down into the pit. The tent was blowing up and down now in the rising wind. It was harder to see into the pit. But there! He moved. The soldier moved! Her heart began to pound as she moved closer to the edge.

CHAPTER 8

A Figure in the Darkness

Then Corina looked down. And there were *three* soldiers. And one was a man who was *alive*.

Corina felt a scream coming. But no sound came out. She just stared down into the pit. Her heart was slamming in her chest. Who was down there? Wang? No, she could see him on guard at the far end of the pit. Suddenly she knew. Someone was after the gold and jewels! He was taking them from the soldiers' bodies! She felt frozen where she stood. Had the man seen her? Was he armed? She had to tell Wang. Corina held her breath and slowly stepped back from the pit. The wind wailed around the corners of the tent. Her heart kept pounding. Slowly she crept along the outside of the pit. Suddenly Wang saw her and came towards her. She put her finger to her lips and pointed towards the pit. Wang looked down, froze. Then he leaned close to Corina.

"Have to get to Wu's phone," he whispered. "Call the police. There may be more of these guys around!"

"I'll go. You stay here and watch him," Corina told Wang. She started towards Wu's car. The wind moaned around her. If she could just get to Wu and Zack. If they would just wake up. If the police would just come!

Suddenly she saw a large dark shape step out of the shadows. A shape she did not know. It was coming towards her. She would never make it to Wu's car. But she had to! The shape came closer. Suddenly Corina picked up a rock. She threw the rock at Wu's car as hard as she could. Crash! The car door opened in a flash. Wu threw himself out of the car. The dark shape was caught in the middle between Wu and Corina. It ran. But suddenly it was tackled by Wu and Zack. They threw the man to the ground.

"There's another man – in the pit!" Corina

yelled. Then she ran for the car cell phone and took it to Wu. He called the police as he and Zack held down the large man.

"I've got this guy," Zack told Wu. "Go help Wang. Corina, are you O.K.?"

"Yes," she answered, her voice shaking. "But Wang – the other man!" Any minute she was sure she would hear a gunshot from the pit. If only the police would get here!

She ran towards the pit. Wu was already inside it. Where was Wang – and the man?

"It's O.K., Corina. Wang has him. Down here," Wu called up to her.

She looked down and saw that Wang had pinned the man to the ground.

Wu climbed out of the pit. "Are you O.K.? That was a close one with that guy by the car. Fast thinking you did – throwing that rock to wake me. If you hadn't, that guy would have held you as a hostage. Would have made Wang let the guy in the pit go to save your life. Zack and I would have slept right through it all. And Wang told me you're the one who spotted the guy in the pit!"

"Yes. But how did he get in there without one of us seeing him?" Corina asked.

"Came across the fields on foot. Left their car on the road. The wind came up and hid any noise they made," said Wu.

Suddenly they heard the wail of police

sirens coming closer. Police cars were swarming into the fields with their spotlights turning. Officers rushed up to Wu and Corina.

"It's all over," Wu told them. "Here are your prisoners." Zack and Wang were pushing the two men forward, their arms pinned behind their backs. "I think they're part of the gang from Bejing (Bay-SHJING) I was worried about."

The police spoke excitedly in Chinese.

"These two are bad business," Wang said. "The police say we're lucky nobody got hurt."

"We're lucky Corina has such sharp eyes. And thinks fast!" Wu smiled. "Things could have gone a lot differently tonight."

"We all owe you one, Corina," Zack said.

"And I always like to repay favors," said Wu. "I have something in mind. Do you think your museum would like to have a show of some clay soldiers this year, Corina?"

"Wu! Yes! That would be fabulous!" said Corina, hugging him. "Thank you, thank you! Wow! Claire will flip! But *you've* got to come over and bring the soldiers. That's part of the deal."

"I think I can arrange that," Wu smiled. "Now let's get you and Zack back to your hotel. Wang will drop you off there."

"But what about you?" Zack asked.

"I think I'll stick around here with the

police for the rest of the night," Wu said. "Today was magical – finding those soldiers. I guess I want to hold onto that a little longer. And thanks to you guys and Wang, the soldiers are still wearing all their gold tonight!"

"Tomorrow we can help you dig," Zack said. "We'll be here early."

"Wait a minute!" laughed Corina. "*How* early? This has been quite a night!"

They waved to Wu as they walked away to Wang's car. They could still see him standing by the pit of the clay soldiers as they drove off into the dawn.